LOKOSHI

LOKOSHI

LEARNS TO HUNT SEALS

Story and lithographs

by RAYMOND CREEKMORE

THE MACMILLAN COMPANY *New York*

1946

LOKOSHI

My name is Lokoshi. I was born in the white Arctic, so far north that only a few people live nearer the North Pole.

Ever since I can remember I have wanted to go on a seal hunt. When I was ten winters old, Ushipi, my father, promised to take me. I needed some warm clothes to wear. My mother made new mukluks, to keep my feet dry, and some warm socks of birdskins with the soft down turned inside. Of course I wore my hooded jacket, fur pants, and big polar-bear mittens.

Early in the morning Ushipi, my papa, got up to prepare the
sledge for the journey to the seal-hunting ice. I brought him a
can of melted snow. That is how we get our water. Papa sprayed
the water from his mouth on the mud-covered wooden runners.
In a minute they were coated with a thin sheet of slick ice.

The whole family helped load the sledge. My cousin Pitzulok
and I caught the dogs and hitched the team. Pitzulok was going
on the hunt too.

Our food and clothes and everything we needed for the hunt were tied to the sledge. We took a saw for making our snow-house—securely fastened in a handy place. Papa cracked his long whip. The dogs jumped and started off. The whole village came to wish us a good hunt with many seals.

The first part of the journey was the hardest, for we had to get from the land down over the rough broken ice to the frozen bay. Pitzulok held the sledge back in steep places, and Papa lifted the runners over the ice blocks when they were in the way. I untangled the dog-team lines when they caught on the ice.

When we reached the flat ice of the bay we could look back and see how the enormous tide lifted the ice as high as five or six sledges, and often left great walls of ice standing when the tide went down.

It was clear and cold, so at first we ran to get warm.

Then we rode. Papa and Pitzulok ran and hopped on the
sledge just as I did. It was great fun. The ice runners make the
sledge easy for the dogs to pull.

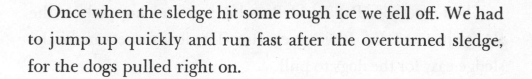

Once when the sledge hit some rough ice we fell off. We had to jump up quickly and run fast after the overturned sledge, for the dogs pulled right on.

After we had been riding a few hours we saw a man a long way off. As we came closer we could see that he was fishing through the ice.

It was Itocha, an old friend of Papa's. We all shook hands and said hello and promised to stop and see his family on our way home.

We passed mountains of ice piled over rocks in the bay.

At this time of year it gets dark quite early, so at five o'clock we started looking for hard-packed snow to build an igloo, where we could spend the night. Papa had found a good bank with his harpoon, and Pitzulok took the saw and began to cut blocks.

Ushipi placed them in a circle around the hole from which the blocks were being cut. Then he cut a notch with his snow knife, with a slant to the top so the next blocks would lean a little.

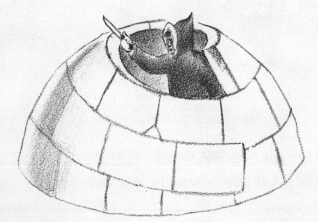

Then the blocks went round and round like a coil of rope—leaning more and more as they neared the top. Papa knew just what to do and he worked fast, setting the blocks so they would not crash down.

As soon as the wall was high enough to keep the wind from blowing it out, we lighted a candle. It threw a warm glow and made it a homey and wonderful camp.

My work was to pack soft snow in the cracks. Only a half-
hour from the time we started cutting the first block our white,
clean home was ready.

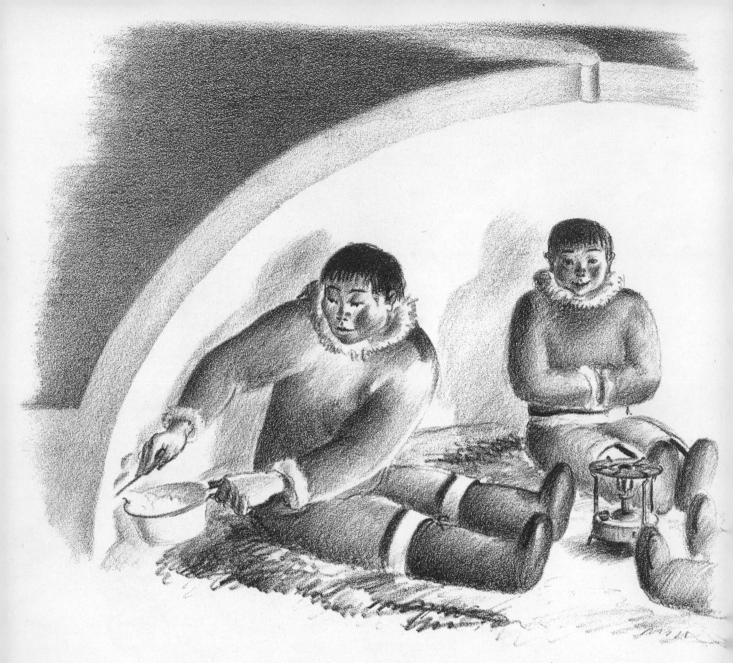

We closed the entrance and spread the furs. We took our
hoods and gloves off and lit the stove. Of course it was very
cold, just a little below freezing, but we felt very warm. Papa
dug clean snow from the side and placed it in a pan over our
stove, and it soon became water. The heat from the cooking
helped to keep us warm

Next morning when we took out the entrance block to go outside, a fierce wind, which we call a williwaw, was blowing. Snow in the wind cut our faces. Frost formed on our eyelids and it seemed as if they would freeze together. Eskimos do not travel in this kind of weather, so we went back to a warm igloo to wait until the williwaw was over.

In three days the williwaw had stopped. A soft snow was falling, so we went on toward the hunting grounds. The dogs were ready to start and pulled at the ropes. When Papa wanted them to go a little to the left or right he would say "Tr-tr-tr-tr-tr," or "Uga-uga-uga-uga-uga."

After a long journey we reached the sealing ice. We saw a
seal come out on the ice a long way off, but when he saw us he
dived in again.

At the sealing camp we met more friends. Some of them had had good hunting. We decided to try our luck the next day.

That night an aurora borealis played its lights across the
sky. When we see these beautiful lights we believe that the
Eskimo spirits are playing ball with a walrus head.

Before light we were ready for the seal hunt. Papa took his harpoon, hunting knife, and several lengths of rawhide line.

The seals come out on the ice to rest in the sun. They sleep about half a minute, then wake to look around. If no enemies are in sight they go back to sleep.

Papa made himself look so much like a seal that when they woke up to look around they couldn't even tell him from one of their own brothers. When the seal went back to sleep he crawled closer. It took many half minutes before Papa came close enough to throw the harpoon.

Every Eskimo man must know how to catch seals, for we can-
not live without them. Our food, clothing, tents, and health
depend on them, so I watched every move the hunters made.

While Pitzulok and Papa hunted, I kept far away and saw many shapes in the snow and ice. In one place the snow looked like breaking seas, but these waves will not fall until the sun is warm enough to melt them in the spring.

In the seal camp I listened to the stories the old men told about the ancient Eskimos. They hunted with walrus-tusk harpoons and cut their snow blocks with stone knives before guns and carpenter's saws were known. I would have liked to stay longer, but our hunt was soon over. We had caught five seals and had to start back with our fine meat.

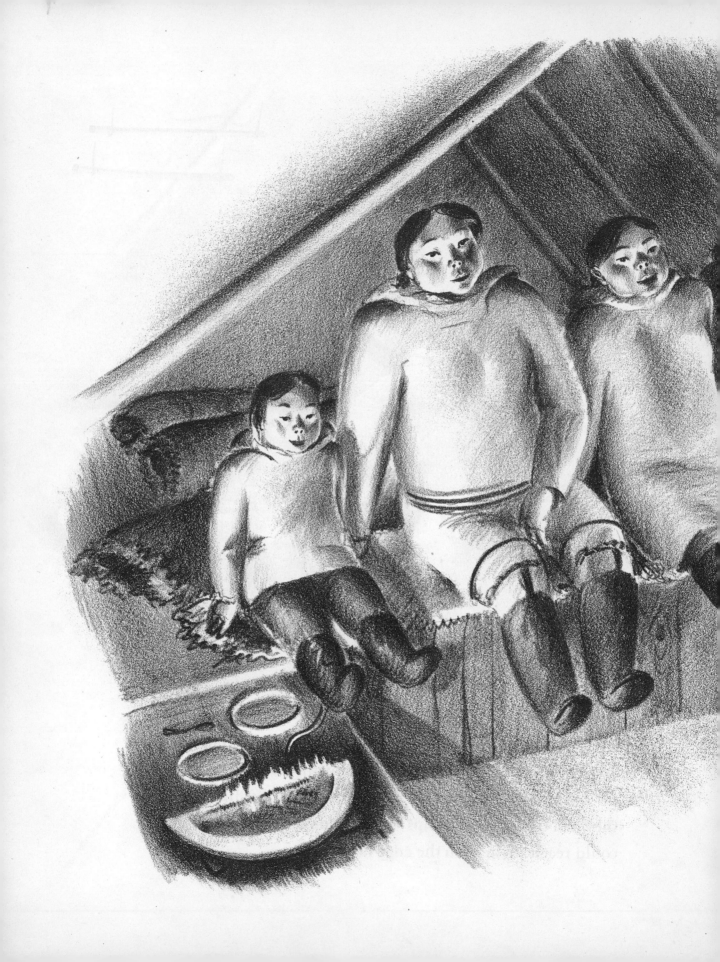

On the way home we stopped to visit Itocha, whom we had
met fishing on the ice. Inside his tent his daughters and sons
sat on the edge of their bed. Their home was just like ours, for
they had two blubber lamps on each side of the entrance. They
could reach them from the edge of the bed.

Now I was anxious to get home, and hurried so fast I slipped on the new ice the high tide had left near the shore. The neighbors waiting for us thought it was much funnier than I did.

Many hands helped us to lift our heavy load of meat up the
bank, for it meant a good feast for all.

Mama and my brothers and sisters were very proud and made
me tell them about the hunt.

A young hunter from our village came home soon after we did. He had luck too, for he had a large snowshoe rabbit and eight ptarmigan. He gave us four birds and we gave his family lots of seal meat to eat, and blubber for their cooking lamps.

   While Mama was cooking our feast we played out in the snow
with our new puppies. They had their own igloo and were lots
of fun.

Our Mama takes great pride in keeping the moss wicks of our blubber lamps just right. While a seal liver and the birds were cooking, she kept a steady flame along the edge of our stone lamp. This will be a great feast.

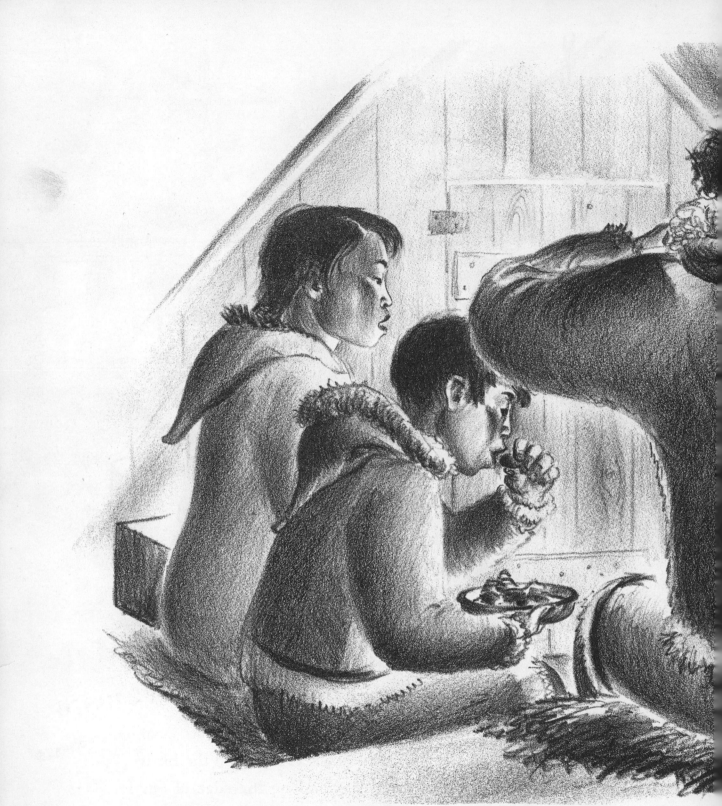

All three children crowded around the pot and each got a
great portion of liver. It was the best part of the seal and was so

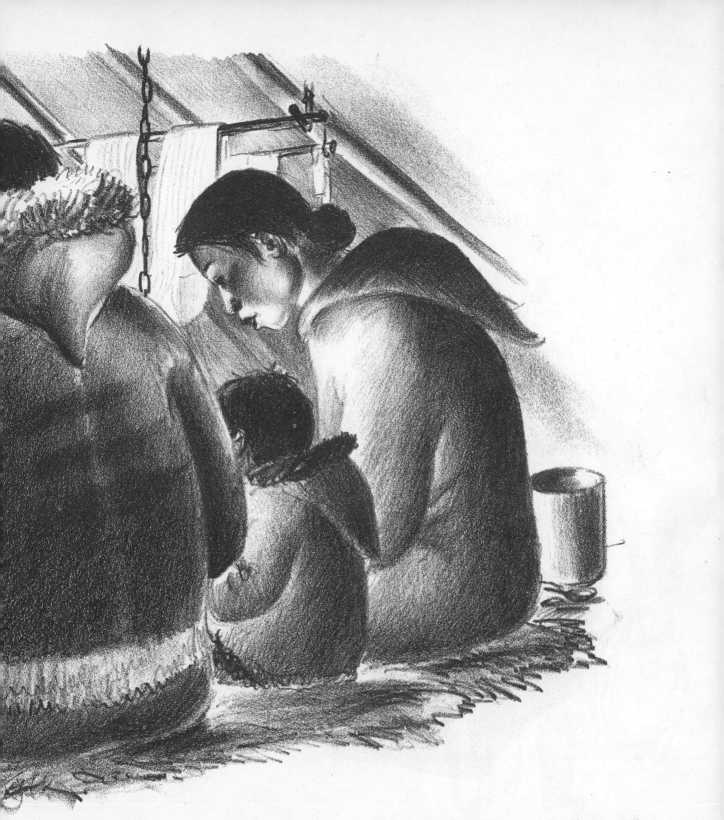

tender it melted like soft snow in our mouths. We ate until we thought we would burst.

The best thing of all came when Papa made a little speech, saying that the trip had proved I would make a good hunter and that as a present I should have the harpoon that we used on the hunt. With it we had caught all the good food we now enjoyed. I was very proud.

1568